MODERN TOSS IX

*from *hitflap*

by Jon Link & Mick Bunnage

interview

I see from your CV that you're bilingual

yeah English and Emoji

health

eu referendum

work

motor show

interview

cheese&wine
this is Jean's latest watercolour from our recent trip to Provence
I reckon my arsehole could do better than that

milestone birthday

do you want to do anything for your milestone birthday coming up?

no I fucking don't

health

legal
longshots

health

Pete Peters
Vigilante Shit Stirrer

Mr Tourette

MASTER SIGNWRITER

now I've retired from professional football I want to give something back to the community via my charitable school of footballing excellence

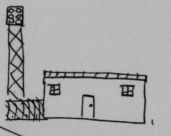

most of all I want a massive sign with the word 'foundation' under my name.

leave it with me

Later...

BIG HEADED CUNT GESTURE

I can see what's gone wrong here, I forgot to tell you my name

I thought I better keep your name off it in case any more of those videos come out of you fucking prostitutes

relationships

liberty taker

work

retail

awkward cunt

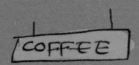

do you want any cakes or pastries with that?

if I wanted them I probably would have fucking asked for them

chill out yeah?

olden days night out

books

PEANUT

DAVID   GARY   PAUL

FOLLOWING THE NEAR VEGETABLISATION OF THEIR SINGER AND SUBSEQUENT DEATHS OF MANY OF HIS BUSINESS ASSOCIATES, THE VOLATILE MOD DUO ARE ON THE LOOKOUT FOR NEW REVENUE STREAMS.

THIS IS GOOD, I'VE JUST HAD AN EMAIL FROM SOME BLOKE CALLED CLIVE WHO WANTS US TO GO ON A VINTAGE ROCKERS TOUR

WHAT'S OUR STATUS ON THE BILLING?

NOT GOOD, LOOKS LIKE HE'S DOING IT IN ALPHABETICAL ORDER. LETS POP ROUND NOW AND SORT IT OUT

I ALWAYS SAID WE SHOULD CHANGE OUR NAME TO 'A PEANUT'

SURELY 'ANUT' IS BETTER?

books

bongo arsehole

medieval brain virus
I think I've been hacked by an evil spirit?
Ok I'm gonna have to ask you a few security questions. What's your mother's maiden name?

health & technology

work

You've Been Nicked

next-door arsehole

identity theft

honest relationship

burials

TOTAL FUCKING DISASTER

in **'Skateboard'**

qualification loophole

I'm getting me dad to sit my business studies exam in return for 25% of my wages if I ever get a job

awkward cunt

work

offline retailer
oi mate how do I get on your wi-fi, just wanna check you're not ripping me off with these prices

clothing technology

work

Pete Peters
Vigilante Shit Stirrer

hello? yeah been wearing a tin foil helmet 24 hours a day for the last year, a couple of weeks ago I took it off for ten minutes just to give me scalp an airing.

pretty sure while it was off, I had a few vague thoughts about the cold war, spies, etc that sort of stuff, you getting the picture? so imagine my surprise when lo and behold barely a month later Steve Spielberg brings out his cold war epic bridge of spies.

not saying I want any cash out of this, and it's obviously too late for a credit on the end titles, so how about a little slip of paper in the Blu Ray release, just outlining my involvement.

let me know if there's going to be a sequel so I can keep me hat on 24-7 till the fucker's been red carpeted, be doing everyone a favour yeah?

apprentishit

retail

I'm not paying 5p for a plastic bag mate,
I'm gonna eat all me shopping here

customer
services

health

I see you've taken yourself off the waiting list for a heart bypass

yeah I managed to talk a vet into having a crack at it

film

oi mate, it's illegal to film in here
I'm not filming I'm watching something else

tv idea found in bin

work

can you just check this email I'm about to send you for any sexist language

travel

it's a nightmare to park, but I get to use the bus lane on the way to work

work

legal
longshots

cocktrepreneur

interview

very impressive reference

cheers I wrote that

dining out

THE FRIENDS OF MODERN TOSS

WE VALUE YOUR PATRONAGE

Sarah Griffiths-Jones, Daniel James, Roger Cowen MA, Dan, Jon 'Shitblistering Wankspanners' Gerrard, Bob Upye, Andy Cuntybollox Smiff, Mead4Speed, *Tramline Quo, see you around, yeah?*, Alison Macarthy, John Appleton, The Moon-Boys of WeyBay, Fred Atkins, Mark Walker - Beloved Aunt, Joe & Sam Wicks, Yeah?, Benjamin Thomas Collier, Steve Haines, Roostie Routs, Paige Perkins, Nat Dugdale. Will Dugdale, Daniel Hall, Will Banks, Sarah Olivier, David Barber, Mark Saville, *****Pauly & Sarah Surridge*****, Malcolm Stoney, Liz West, Vicky Byers, Jason Crabsticks, Andy Williams, Richard Utter Tosser Morris, I hate Matt Harmer, Andrew Gallimore, Horatio Hornblower-Joynson, Chris Dunne, Marcus Rann, Tim Roberts, This one's for Snax, Jason Barlow, Scott McLennan Pirie, Casper aka crumpet aka monster shit hit 27/04/16, Eddie Flippance, Alex Nganga Papamichael, Darren Smith, Matt from ANATOMY, Adrian Milliner, Julia Nightingale, Alex Nicholson, Otto Haywards shit butler, Adam Edward Parker, Ian Cottingham, Chris Williams, James Matthews, Jimmy O, Tori Leatherland, Marc Jones, Michael Byrne, Matty Cunting Wright, Sean and Amy Fairhurst, Emma Lewis, Danger Roberts, Kelly Rodger Smith, Donald Soutar, STEPHEN J KING ESQ, MARIE 'marjorie baxter stewart' KING", Steve McGhie - yeah?, Tits McGee, Peter J Sommese, Dave Tennyson, SUE HARDY, sir Fletcher Phelps, Chris Hall, shrff, Chris Pack, Ben Ikin, Libby Woodland, Tim Frost, Martyn James, Emma Hogarth, Kevin Hill, Mr. Nick 'Baldy' Davies, Allen Pollard, Tony Clough: The Western Hemisphere's Leading Cunt, Peter 'Fucking Arsehole' Phillippo, Marcus Tustin, Paul 'Tosser' Timlett, Lee Barlow, sickBocks, Simon Davis, Charles McFadyen, Scott Harris, Jonathan Simpson, Greg Bell, JudgeDewie, Robin Cunting Fulford, Tony Blaker, Ant Brett, SilverbackRF, Philip Harris, Kevin V Johnson, Sarah and Jason Edwards, Jonners, Sam Hillage, Mike Hyde, Chris 'Chumley' Swannie, Gordon Fudge, Josh Lumb, Dan Allan, Sophie Ramuz, Martyn Warren, Jamie Michael Bivard, Chris Gooch, Doug Quelch, Graham Thomas, Troy Fucking Goatley, YesTom, Mark Miller, Mr Stephens, Ian Hodgson, David Caunt, Jon 'Dave's brother' Goodwin, the boy Crump, Jeremy Finch, *Happy Birthday Sturtz, 60's not that old!*, J&GJordan, Neil Elkins, Matthew Alexander Kaufman, Simon Adams, Louise Jordan, Fraser Mann, Ian McFee, Rob Harris, Matt Knoyle, Paul G Burke, Bonesun(!), GJH, Hagrid, Lee Rooney, Dan Sims, Hubbawelcome, Leonie (Flytalk) Wallace, Suzanne (I want to marry Mr.Tourette) Curran, Jimmy Fenn, David Grievson, Paul Thomsen Kirk, Mark Maplethorpe, ed tombs, *Baz Floyd, yeah?*, ZOWIE DRYDEN, Robert Allen, Peter Frank Agnew, Lindsay Rutland, Clive Oxford Yeah!, Ben Pearce, Surly McGitface, Mike Rothwell, THE GRANT PHILPOTT, David Armitage, Claire Syrett, Fraser 'Grizzly' Gillespie, Kevin, Adrian Zak (NOT Zak Adrian) yeah?, Kathryn Macdonald, Matt Lander, Mr. Christopher e Holden!, Dale McCarthy, Richard Jenner, harriet bedford, *Dan Harrison, yeah?*, Mr. Karl de Vroomen, Chris Westwood, Lee Dewhurst, JoJoJu Edgson, Geraint Morris, Mat Elliott, Grinxtrel Print, Charlie Wise, Donald Mullis, Vanessa Bell, Happy Fathers Day Tom Billington, Jon... that ginger cunt, Mark West, Lowri Rhys, Aaron Taylor-Cotter Still Wants Paying, Turbosalad, Steve Austin, Rik Frost, Barrie Hemsley, SOFT ALAN, Steve 'You're welcome, arsehole' Horn, Ia Fucking Rouse, Freya Williams, Martin Jarvis, Dave 'bit of a cunt' Whyte, Mr C & Lisa P, Diana, Geoff 'panty thief' Crease, Winchy, Dan Rebellato, Thatch Park, Saundra O'Shea, Mikey P, Steve 'Max Wyrtle' Evans, Edd Hindley, Tom Rolf' Hindley, Stephen McNamara, Mr Rick Danvers, Iain Page, Andy Napier, Graeme Stewart, Banc Media, Carl O'Bogtrotter O'Connell, Jo 'Cockwomble' Smith, Steve 'ocky' Mingle, The Boofs of Ealing, Jonathan 'two sheds' Davis, Lauren Swift, ADRIANO 'WOLF' CATTINI, Luke Miller, Liza Bate, Dave Johnson, Lee Burnett, Peter Gray, brian whitehorn, Amelia Charman, **STRUMSKI**, Steve, Tim Hammerton & Diane Ratcliffe, Lost in Greenwich, Gary not making tea any more? Robards, Benjamin Sebastian Baxter, Rebecca Johnson, Jon & Natasha Fielden, Colonel Chinstrap, 'Tall Paul' Roberts, Chris Hayes, Wayne Lump, *Mike, Yeah?*, Sir AdamJS Esq., Anne, Stephen and Eleanor Curran - wearing roller skates now, yeah?, Hamish Crooks, Saul 'what does it look like?' Taylor, Neil Tune, Gary Copson, Ben Morley, Viscount Gary Montagu Coyne, VICKY&NEIL, Emma Holohan, PIG, Ian Clifford, Jonee Elwood, raine, Christopher Cockroft, Dave Evans, Jason & Liz, Frank Rooney, Geraint Rogers, Steve Sakal, Simon Pinner, Stephen Pinner, Richard 'Fat Bloke'Harris, Kenny McDonald, Ray McColl, Matt Morden, Oscar Nash, James the Amazing, Gaz Sharpe, Chris Holt, Julia and Antony Silson, Debbie and Andy Ellison, Benny Big Bollocks Griffiths, Vicki Patient, Danny O'Hare, Graham Ward, Jeremy Booth, Charlotte, JPF, Nick Cresswell, Gerard Papasimakopoulos, Lawrence Camm, Sir Rich & Lady Emily of Bournemouth, Lee Hemming, Darren Hubbard, Michael Ehrmantraut, Rossy, Kate-Pac, Stan, JAMIE KEDDIE, Addison Evans, James Carrington, Eve & Luke Ferry-Bolder, Jim Tyler, Dan Waters, Daniel Miller, Negweewee Miller, Motherbird Miller, Mr.stephen brooker, Kay Hender, Pete Weston, Emma Burke, Jimmy don't forget to print my name this time yeah Goulding, Karen Falconer, Howard Greenwood, Melanie Nash, Eoin O'Connor, Robin Lawson, Colin Hudd, Miles 'I'M OVER HERE YOU CUNT' Paterson, #JimJamWed, Martin Middleton, Neil, Nursey O'Townsend, Iain 'I'm the king' Wareham, Gary Grice, Jimmydids, Stuart Dudman, Al Hunter, yeah, John Bateson, Louise Harvey, Dave Spencer, Tony Chandler, JAMES MOSELEY, Frank Reynolds Yeah, ELTON 'Go for it, yeah?' LAM, Colin Cole-Johnson, KEVIN FUCKING LOWRIE IN MASSIVE LETTERS, Pete Gaskill, John Guzzardi, David 'Council Tit Gristler' Frettsome, Team Davies, (Shoreham-by-Sea Branch), Dani 'bunhead' Harris is a fucking booml, love harrow x, Rael Duncan, Paul Gregson, Chris I broke my leg dancing to SKA Bruce!, Marc O'Day, Kate Deacon, Adrian Wilcox, Miles Bullough, Gareth Gamble, Jodie Morrichild and Ben Lawperson, Nick Hill, Keith 'Bambi Killer' Atkinson, Duncan Hall, Steve P, Richard Pedrick, Mathew Prior, Pete Hammond Smells of Piss, Yeah!, Birthday girl Alli Perry, Luke Whiffen, SARAH, JAMES AND FLOSSIE Yeah!, Catherine Cluett, Nathan Jones, Ian Irving, Rob 'Yeah?' McNeill, Mark 'Spartacus' Brown, Colin 'Birthday Boy' Brown, Robin still fucking miserable Evans, Beloved Aunt, Paul Jackman, Rob Phokus, Rob Lascelles, Damien Schmidt, Al Wood, Ben Halliwell, Kate of Kate Hall, PAUL S J MARTIN, Martin Bate, Nathan Barnett, Richard Ansell, Zoe Harrison, Dickie Woods, James Beat, Noah Jack Dingwall, Marc Prior, @SiKehoe, The K mother fucking G, Baby Bella Ras, Chris Tucker, PAUL CORCORAN, Annessa, Patto!, DaveDotDanks, Nick Reilly, Catherine Hunter-James, Jim Merrett, Mr and Mrs Goodwin, Pete Amour, G. O'Keefe, Lady Lynsey V, Andy Holden, Matt Holden, Kimi Huang, Jon Raine, Matt Searle, Simon 'FuckingCockAyss' Turner, Elsie Charlie, Rhys Lightning Gibson, yeah?, Cath Anderson, Sanjay Dhiman, Spencer House, Henry Burton, Kate Grant Mitchell and the Aggy Alan Fam, John Cullen, Sharon Trickett, Grant Fergusson, Stew Hall, Lisa Bradley, Ashley Mcavoy, Matthew 'yea F*cking looks like it 'n all' Knights, Lee Mullin, Gareth Jones, Cunty McCunt Mullis, Liam Bevan, Jessica Morley, Barry Jameson, Chris (Not the one that beat Rihanna) Brown, That Twat Reynolds, Rachypoos Redfern, Crusty Mcpumpernickel, Adrian Sheehan, Andy Chad, StuartKempEsq, Calvin Leckey, Francis Watson Armstrong, Simon Ward, Bill Stephens, Gary Laser Eyes, Tom and Val Bannoch, Joe Gibson, Princess Samantha Kilmartin, Jonah Haines, Fi Donovan, Gary James, Rosie James, Dan Fagg, Steve Martin, Sarah Watt, Maffhew and Whalter Trainshpotter, Simon Warr, MIKE STAFFORD IN CAPITALS, Turdi Smallbank, mark hunter, Matthew Keen, Roberto Buono, Gary Hughes, Stew Bryant, Tom 'Badger Bastard, I LOVE TAITY' White, Jim Allen, David Kevan Brown, Fat Taity, Joel Nesbitt, Michael Keogh, Dom Liddell, Rebecca 'Speculum Crusher' Mundon-Carter, Rachel, Tom Stubbs, Mick Hare, James Fielding, Charles & Margaret's Mickey Rooney Emporium, Huntly Thomas, Dylfin, Mejoolienfn, Russell 'Rusticles' Dean, Mark Cazaly, BIG JEZ, Clive Fucking Moys, Tom Smith, yeah?, Rob Caunt with an a, yeah?, Michael Cole, Prince Babu, Ant 'I read it on the shitter' Farmer, Christoffer Gniechwitz, Anica Meiland, The Hair Ratters of Vanbrugh Court, Alex Garston, Brian 'Dennis is an arsehole' Clint, Benny Large (Big shot on the South Coast), Matthew Cattee, Nick Spencer, BEN GOLDING, Yvette V. Warburton, Del Buck, The Joe/Jo Collective, A. Maria Ramirez, Derek Bell, Steven McDade, Ian Fuckpig Williamson, Janel Rooney McFadyen, Jill Reedman, Simon Ward, Jude Bahnan, DW 'Yeah?, James theholyllama Russell, Brunners, Iain Lockey, Sam Duggan, Neil Colman, douglazy, Andrew Tebbenham, Damien Warburton, Martin Ruddy, STEPHEN 'All These People Want To Be My Friend Too' MARTIN, Phil Keefe, Jonathan Pearson aka Jukeboxjohnnie, SIR IAIN PANDA ARSEBISCUIT McJOBBY II, Mr Stuart Wilson, Pat Porter Yeah, Josh Harwood, Rob 'Homeboycie' Borland, Simon McCullough, Riaad van der Merwe, Alison Walster yeah, John 'Horace' Summers, Mr Thomas Giles Walker, Daniel Willcox, James 'insert shit nickname here yeah?' McConnell, Sir And His Slut, Mats Frederikson Jeris Sykovas, Emily Walters, Rob Ford, Tooney, Tom O'Loughlin, Monster Ronson, Jonathan SYNTH Stephens, Oliver 'the big nosed prick' Joyce, olivier robin, Ian HUMPTY Humphreys, Alan You Wanker, Marcus The Kiwi, JD Laux, Ian Goldsmith, Steve 'poster boy for Stupid Is As Stupid Does' Potz-Rayner, Twatbags McGonagle, Perry fucking Hunt, yeah!, Dorota Cuntflaps, NICK BALDACCI, Alison Newman, George-David Tomlinson, emjemjemjem, MANGROVE, Richard Alden, Edmundo Andrews, Darren Middleton, WOOHOO IanPaulMarsh, Matt Jobling and Laurel Temmel, Paul 'Barrel Hunter' Knight, Samantha Tang, Reverend Ram Rod Tod, STEEB, Zoe Richmond-Smith and Mike Ashworth, David Mackenzie, Shifty Cunt Steve, Dave 'Cunty McCuntFace' Spendley, Gary Bassett, Dr Rob 'you cunt' Morley, Mrs Jake's Painting & Decorating Services, Vita Ruby, Andrew Maxfield, Mark Wheatley, Johnny Boyd, PORTSLADE DAVE YEAH!, Rob Downie, Chris Bragg, Matt the Greek, Pamela Glennie, JAMES SIMPSON, Ben 'The Dutchman' Brown, Robin Barnard, Martin Brown, Ali Mantell, cheers!, Mark Platt, Wright, Gallichan & Wright, missing pets a speciality, Neil 'Fifteen' Conner, Gary McConnell, for fuck's sake, Hugh & Hilde (In Belgium yeah?), Meester Bond, Max 'shitted up' McAllister, Ed Boucher, Ben Rowe, Philip Turrell, Tamara Young, James Rowe, Jonny Bongo, Jonny Hall, Steve Smithard, Mark Himsworth, Hello Baby Smarks, Anthony Maude, BRAVE STUBBY, David Renfrew, Chris, ::BOB PULLEN::, Carl Foreman, FRIEND_NAME_HERE, Becki 'Shitnak' Gilberthorpe, yeah?, Charlotte Cook, BLONDIE ROBERTS & JOLYON GOBBLIN, Phil Miller, JT 'IT LOOKS BIGGER IN THE LIGHT' Tynan, Starla Jet MacDonald, Darren Startup, james upson, Alex Lawson, Matt Baywatch, KUNT, Simon Smith, Andy 'Hoggy' Hogg, Jez Burn, **Emma Louise! Marry me yeah? Nice one. See ya!**, Ben Neary, RICH PARSONS, Ross Neary, Martin Watson, Ian Funnell, SIMON MAESTRO DAVIES, Matthew Hawthorne, Colin Polly, Dolly Dixon and Lupin Lamb, simon waller, Bonbonyeye, Phil Williams, Matt (Le Ginge) Jones, Chris Plumley, Mick Jeavons, WavyDavy Smith, Kidge Kidgell, IF YOU SLICE A TOMATO AND THROW IT IN A BUCKET OF SHIT AND COVER THE SLICES WITH A BIT MORE SHIT, YOU GET SHITLOADS OF TOMATOES. THIS MESSAGE WAS BROUGHT TO YOU BY DAN & ROYAL AUGEY, THE BEST AUGEYS IN THIS TERRIBLE WORLD FULL OF BOMBS AND DEATH. STOP READING BOOKS, Tom Price, Steve Morrell, Richard Midwinter, Jim Christian, John Barrow, Ian 'The Gibbon' Hunter, Neddy Devil, Iain 'Dor-Iain Grey' Wilson, Mark Ogilvie, George Nicolas, Caroline Holmes, Charlie Easterbrook, Greg Mansell, Andrew Bird, Will McManus, Aidan Fitzpatrick, AndyLurve1964..bought a comic yeah?!, Kevin 'Nobba' White, Daniel Chambers, Jennifer Chambers, David 'gamingdave' Robinson, Doak and McCreddie, yeah?, The.Liz, Dreenagh Darrell, Michael Bryant, Matt Dixon, MATT FAIRHALL, ALEX JACKSON, Matt Lucock, Steggs and Lisa, thatandywhite, Andrew Carlin, Richard Hitt, Andrew Fouracre, JAMES TWEEDIE YEAH?!, Rich, Alex Fraser, RIVET HEAD, Fred Furse, Jeremy E, David Mark Harris, Felicity Reardon, Ed Tolley, Mij Walker, Julie Tait, dopskop, Mark Stent, Thomas Panadason, Ruby 'Really don't think that is appropriate Dad' Croney, Edric Ellis, The Reverend Sibediah Wilberforce Hyrebediah, Philip John, Rob Halloway, Richard 'Where the fuck is Mr Tourette?' Paul-Jones, Warren & Laura Rossiter, 12yrsAngelWilliamsBumbumbia, Gareth Barton, Steve Townsend, Writing Gaz Lee in the back of a book yeah!?, Stewart Killala, MR DAVID JOHN ANDREW WOOD esq., Richard, The Delightful Sausage, Ciaran O'Carroll, Stewart Nolan, JONATHAN KNOWLES, Darryl Smith, GRAEME LANGLANDS, The Deckchairs, Captain Billy Firebeard, Jim Barwick, Dave Thompson, Angry Warthog & Spacebee Inc, Bobby Pegg, Richard Milne, Ben Golding, Adam Martin, Annice Larsen, David Blakey & Anna Adam, Gar Samuel, DFR, Nick Kenny, Simon Fox, Charlie cha cha le bona Abbott, Rob Colley, Mathew Nagel - like Bagel but with an N, Dr Andrew Turner, Anthony Fucking Rees, Alistair Trueloye, Samuel Muppet, Reuben & Cooper Davies, Captain Shittywipers Henderson, Harry Moore, Eoin O'Connor, Dara Maguire, Rob Green, Jim O'Connor, Jason Slattery, yeah?, David Attew, Dan Attew, Ever-Jan ël'm a Lying Dutch Cunt Psycho and Managing Cunt Directori Hentenaar, Simon (Colin Dentaaaaaaay is a legend) Fenn, Susie Blackburn, SS Mummy, Josh Tacchinella Newman, Randhir Kang, Sarah & Patrick Palmer, Kevin Trepess, Tim Whiteman, Michael ëThe Beardí Blay, Jamie McCall, Neepa the Slacker, Daniel Baker, Andrew Micklethwaite, STYLES - yeah bitch, Grant Mainwaring, Jules Joseph, Ed Barrett, Mac, Liz Lord, Sue Gardner, Peter Round-Thebush, Kenneth The Hen, Tim and Donna awkward Northern cunts..., Guybrush Threepwood, Darren ëPinot Noirí Middleton, EmmaJason4eva, Helen Briscoe, Bryan Richardson, Garth James, Ricky Wells, George Hare, Chris ëDa Catís Papaí Ko, Mike Bromage, Fran Moore, TOM BREAKS, J.R, Wobbut ther Wascal?, Timbo Havard, Bryan Janes, SEAN BRADY, Dean Baldwin, Adam Peach, Toby Walker, John Manson, Keith Wallace, James Huntington, Cunty Dan, Bert Quock, NEIL FUCKING OXON IN CAPITALS, Dave Rush, Mark 'Gunner' Gallen, Idwell Parry Jones - The Welsh Ambassador, Stephen 'Brownie' Brown, Kevin Sloane, Nick Sandbrook, Anna Hyde, Phil Rolfe, Ray Jones if you much fucking know, Richard Ashdown, Helen 'Give 'em the ole razzle dazzle' Marsden, Paul Ridley McRidleyface, Ciaran Clarke, Barry Gridley, Paul Griffin, general morris, Wazza, ANNE MARTIN, Gerard Papasimakopoulos, Fuck ya people!, Stephen Potter, Steve Lord of Cowickshire Smyth, Mark Thompson, Sandy Palmer, Barry Elliott, Alan Bremner, Dylan Turner, Warby, Barry 'hoofwanking bunglecunt' Mooring, Benny 'cock wombling, fuck nugget' Collins, Nick Sandbrook, Kevin Sloane, Dave Whyte, Chris 'Noaks' Noakes, Beeky, Andy 'Arthur Fag' Fernandez, Amjid Alam, Matt Gamblin.